C000120947

A GUIDE TO THE

INDUSTRIAL ARCHAEOLC

OF THE BOROUGH OF ELMBRIDGE

Compiled by Rowland G.M. Baker

Supervising Editor: Francis Haveron

Illustrations: Rowena Oliver

Cartography: Steven A. Baker

Surrey Industrial History Group

1989

FOREWORD

This is the third booklet of a series being published by the Surrey Industrial History Group describing the industrial archaeological remains to be found in the County of Surrey. Because this is a formidable task, the method is to use the existing district council areas created in 1974. Booklets covering the Reigate and Banstead area and the Waverley area have already been published. Subsequent booklets will in time cover the remaining areas and eventually a hardback book will be published for the whole County.

Because of the outstanding national importance of the Brooklands site, it has been dealt with in separate articles from material supplied by the Brooklands Society and the Brooklands Museum to whom I send grateful thanks.

Francis Haveron (Series Editor)
Surrey Industrial History Group,
Surrey Archaeological Society,
Castle Arch, Guildford, Surrey.

About the author.

ROWLAND BAKER,1920-1987

As the son of the village policeman, he was brought up in Molesey and lived there for most of his life. By profession he was an electrical engineer. He joined the Surrey Archaeological Society in 1948 and wrote a paper on the Hampton Court bridges for it in 1961. He was a founder member of the Esher Society and published "The Book of Molesey" in 1966. He made special studies of insurance company plaques and the City of London coal and wine tax posts. He also wrote three of the "Walks" series round East Molesey, Thames Ditton and Weston Green.

Copyright 1990: text - Rowland G.M. Baker and the Surrey Industrial History Group ; drawings - Rowena Oliver, Pamela Haveron and J.Kenneth Major.

ISBN : 0 9509697 3 7

THE INDUSTRIAL ARCHAEOLOGY OF THE BOROUGH OF ELMBRIDGE

CONTENTS

WARNING.
Many of the sites listed are on private property and permission to
view must be sought from the owners. Note also that the descriptions
and uses of the buildings, sites or objects are those when last viewed
by the author or the supplier of the information.

LIST OF ILLUSTRATIONS

Cover. Speed at Brooklands ! John Cobb driving the Napier Railton car at Brooklands in 1937. Cobb held the lap record at a speed of 143.44 mph and was also World Land Speed Record holder at nearly 400 mph.

Inside front cover. Map of the Borough of Elmbridge.

A NOTE ON THE GRADING OF BUILDINGS

Scheduled Ancient Monuments are protected by the various Ancient Monument Acts from 1913 onwards. Ownership of such a site means that the owner must give three months notice to the Secretary of State of any intended demolition, removal or repair. Unauthorised activity is liable to fines, imprisonment or both.
Statutory lists of buildings of special architectural or historic interest are prepared by the Secretary of State for the Environment under Section 54 of the Town and Country Planning Act of 1971. The lists are continually being re-assessed. Buildings are classified as Grade I,II*, II or L as follows:
Grade I : buildings of outstanding interest (only about 4% of listed properties.)
Grade II* : particularly important buildings of their type or period
Grade II : buildings of special interest (the main bulk of listed properties)
Grade L : Local listing of lesser quality than Grade II but of importance to the local area.

A GUIDE TO THE INDUSTRIAL ARCHAEOLOGY OF

THE ELMBRIDGE AREA.

A. WATERMILLS.

The River Mole has been an important source of power for almost as long as man has been settled along its banks. Domesday Book listed some twenty mills on the river in 1086, and its waters turned the wheels of at least six mills within the area now forming the Borough of Elmbridge.

1. Cobham - Downside Mill. (TQ118583)
   Originally the mill of the manor of Downe, the site has been used for a number of purposes - grinding corn, paper, iron and tinplate manufacture, producing flock, and the generating of electricity. The present U-shaped brick and tiled structure dates from the eighteenth century, but many other buildings have been demolished. Several weirs and sluices remain, together with portions of a large water wheel, smaller wheels, connecting rods and gears. The mill stands on a remote stretch of the Mole, approached only by a long private road. Permission should be obtained before any attempt is made to view the site.

2. Cobham - Cobham Mill. (TQ122599)
   A well-known landmark on the A 245 road leading from Cobham to Stoke d'Abernon. Before 1951 two mills stood side by side with waterwheels between. The older mill was then demolished to straighten the course of the road, a sacrifice to the ubiquitous motor car and an undoubted advantage for road transport but an irrevocable destruction of a very pleasant visual harmony. The remaining building of brick with tiled gables dates from about 1820. Unlike Downside, the career of this mill has always been linked to the grinding of corn, which continued until the 1920's. Much of the machinery still survives, but the wheels lie a-mouldering outside. The mill is a listed Grade II building, and the Cobham Conservation Group has plans to restore both it and the machinery

3. Esher - Esher Mill. (TQ132658)
   Like most mills on the Lower Mole, this, too, has had a chequered history - corn, brass wire, iron, paper, linoleum, bookbinding and light industry. There was even an attempt at one time to use it as a gun-cotton factory. For a long period there were probably two mills on the site, corn grinding and industrial use proceeding simultaneously. The history of the place chronicles a series of disastrous fires - in 1853, 1877, 1898, 1902, 1908, and the last in an adjacent workshop in 1978. After this the whole site was cleared, the buildings demolished and the estate let out for the erection of individual

Figure 1. The original Cobham Mill. (A2)

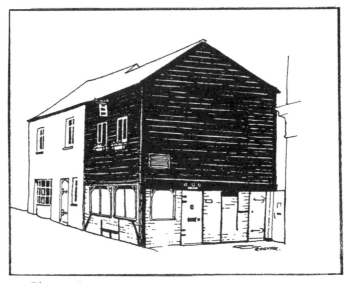

Figure 2. Former smithy at East Molesey. (C 13).

light industrial units. When the mill was knocked down,
three large water turbines were discovered intact beneath
the floor. These were investigated and recorded by members
of the Surrey Industrial History Group, but their
preservation or removal was considered to be impracticable,
and they were left in situ encased in concrete.

4. Thames Ditton - Ember Mill. (TQ146673)
    This mill stood on the River Ember, a branch of the
Mole, named from the manor of Ember or Imber, by which it
flowed. After the usual start as a manorial corn mill, its
history is very much combined with that of Esher Mill, in
the manufacture of brass and iron wire. It was demolished
about 1837. The island on which the mill was
erected, together with the sluices and waterfalls on either
side, are all that is left to denote the site. They may be
seen from the nearby footbridge. The new channel recently
constructed as part of the flood prevention scheme
by-passes the site completely, but a small flow is allowed
to percolate into the old course to keep the stream looking
as it was. A sketch of the mill as it appeared in the mid
1820's may be seen in the extra-illustrated version of
Manning and Bray's History of Surrey in the British
Library.

5. East Molesey - Upper Mill. (TQ144676)
    The two mills of East Molesey, Upper and Lower, are
associated respectively with the manors of Molesey Matham
and Molesey Prior. They were both concerned in an
acrimonious lawsuit in 1215. During the Commonwealth they
were both acquired for the manufacture of gunpowder, which
the Upper Mill continued to produce until about 1780, when
the various outbuildings were incorporated into the grounds
of East Molesey Park. The islands on which the workshops
stood, together with the various weirs, sluices and
waterfalls, now form part of the ornamental gardens of a
house called "The Wilderness", the sports club of the
Chartered Bank.

6. East Molesey - Lower Mill. (TQ153682)
    Soon after the restoration of the monarchy in 1660, the
Lower Mill, sometimes called Sterte Mill, ceased to be used
for gunpowder making (probably its situation opposite the
royal palace of Hampton Court may have had some influence
in this), and it reverted to a corn mill. The old rambling
timber structure was replaced by the present brick building
in the 1820's. Besides corn grinding, it has also been
used as a saw mill, for the manufacture of "Zenith" motor
cycles, as a tent works, and for other purposes. It is now
best seen from the bridge over the Ember in Hampton Court
Way.

7. Weybridge - Thames Lock Mill. (TQ073655)
    This mill, otherwise called Ham Haw Mill or Weybridge
Mill, stood at the junction of the River Wey and the Wey

Navigation, and was originally constructed in the late
seventeenth century for the production of paper, later used
for flour, brass and iron work, and for oil seed crushing.
The old structure was demolished some years ago, and the
site is now occupied by industrial works. A copper penny
was issued by the owners in 1812 when it was an iron
manufactory, which displays a good illustration of the mill
as it then was.

B. MINERAL EXTRACTION.

8. Gravel Working.
The extraction of sand, gravel and ballast takes place,
or has taken place, in various locations all over the
Borough and has done so for centuries. It would be
impossible to list them all. They range from the small pits
maintained by the former parochial authorities to the
massive commercial enterprises for building materials seen
today. Most of the worked out sites have been re-instated,
and there must be many people who little realise that the
estate on which their nice new house stands was but a few
years ago the middle of a gravel pit.

9. Glass sand.
Very fine sand for glass making was at one time mined
from beneath Esher village, and the tunnels left after the
digging ceased often puzzle the residents when they come
upon them today.

10. Brickworks.
The band of clay running across the Borough, known as
Claygate Beds, yields a material ideally suited for the
making of bricks, tiles and the like. As early as 1782,
Parliament gave powers to dig on Cobham and Walton Commons
for soil to produce bricks for rebuilding Cobham Bridge. A
number of brickfields were formed around the district, all
now closed, but some claypits still survive as ponds. One
brickfield, that on the eastern side of Oaken Lane,
Claygate, was utilised during the First World War by the
Royal Engineers for experiments with machinery intended for
the construction of trenches and tunnels close to, or even
under, the enemy's lines. Some of the tunnels still exist.
(See SIHG Newsletter, No. 24, 1984, pp.5-7).

C. MISCELLANEOUS INDUSTRIES.

Forges.

At one time every village had at least one forge where the
skill of the smith and farrier were practised. The
following buildings which still exist were originally
smithies but are now utilised for other purposes:-

11. Claygate - Common Road. (TQ161635)
A timber and corrugated iron building occupied by a

member of the same family that ran it as a forge, but now
it is used for the servicing and repair of lawnmowers.

12. Cobham - Portsmouth Road. (TQ103604)
    A brick, timber and tiled building, behind No. 45
Portsmouth Road, now used by a builders' merchant.

13. East Molesey - 150 Bridge Road. (TQ150680)
    A timber framed building used as a smithy until the
1930's, now occupied by a firm of printers.

14. Esher - West End Lane. (TQ127635)
    A brick building now incorporated with a private house
(Chequers).

15. Hersham - Pleasant Place. (TQ115640)
    A brick building now part of a private bungalow.

Brewing.

There is no commercial brewing carried out at present
within the Borough but the following buildings once used
for the purpose still survive:-

16. Esher - West End Lane. (TQ129639)
    A brewery is mentioned here as early as 1841, although
the present red-brick structure dates from later in the
century, possibly from when the site was taken over by
Watneys in 1899. Brewing ceased during the First World
War, and the premises were taken over by a coal merchant.
At the present time they are unoccupied and in a very
parlous state.

17. Thames Ditton. (TQ164666)
    Some of the buildings forming part of the brewery remain
behind the off-licence at the junction of Giggs Hill Road
and Portsmouth Road. Brewing ceased in 1911, and the
machinery was offered for auction.

Film making.

18. Walton-on-Thames - Film studios. (TQ 098664)
    Cecil Hepworth, an early pioneer of moving pictures,
started making films in a house in Hurst Grove in 1899, and
gradually as production increased, spread out until he had
taken over much of the surrounding property. The only
building still surviving is that now used as the Walton
Playhouse, constructed in 1920 to house two 800 kilowatt
diesel generators which Hepworth had acquired from a
captured German U-boat, to supply the studios with lighting
and power. The business was acquired in the mid 1920's by
Nettlefold Studios, and thereafter many well-known cinema
and television films were produced here. Production ceased
in the mid 1960's, at which time the site was reputed to be
the oldest cinematograph studios in the kingdom.

Boat Building.

19. West Molesey - Platts Island. (TQ138692)
In 1889 the lower half of the island was acquired by a
firm called Immisch & Co. to exploit the idea of its
founder, a pioneer electrical engineer named Moritz
Immisch, to run a fleet of electric launches. These were
built on the island and powered by batteries.
Charging stations were positioned at strategic locations
up the Thames, mostly on floating platforms, but that at
Platts Island was by far the largest and most important.
It included a steam-driven generating station, the
buildings of which still stand, and which also supplied
power to the nearby Hurst Park race-course. The business
was ruined by the advent of petrol-driven motor-boats;
noisier, smellier but more reliable. The premises were
then taken over by Messrs. Thorneycroft for boat building
and during the First World War they produced their renowned
motor torpedo boats, in one of which a Victoria Cross was
won. This boat with the medal painted on its side was
preserved on the island until 1967 when Thorneycrofts moved
to Southampton. The ground at the upper end of the island
is raised considerably by receiving the spoil excavated
from the construction of the reservoirs on the mainland.
The water authority extracts water by pumping from the
gravel beneath the island, and which is thereby partly
filtered.

Engineering.

20. Thames Ditton - Ferry Works. (TQ161673)
This factory was originally constructed by the engineers
Willand and Robinson in 1879, but much was rebuilt after a
disastrous fire in November 1888. The reconstructed
building utilised a "saw-tooth" north light roof, the
earliest known example of the application of this technique
to the construction of a machine shop. In 1911, after the
firm had moved to Rugby and been absorbed by the English
Electric Company, the premises were taken over by Messrs.
Auto Carriers, makers of the the well-known A.C. cars.
After the last war, they produced three-wheeled Ministry of
Pensions invalid cars and, based on the same design, a
private car called the "Petite", the bodies of both of
which were made from fibreglass. The works have now been
divided among a number of small enterprises.

D.PUBLIC SERVICES.

Water.

21. Cobham - Downside parish pump. (TQ112579)
In Downside Common Road, it was erected in 1858 by
Harvey Combe, the local squire, for the benefit of the
inhabitants who had no water supply of their own.

Figure 3. Cobham - Downside.
Parish pump. (21)

OPENING OF THE NEW WORKS OF THE LAMBETH WATER COMPANY, SEETHING WELLS, DITTON.

[C 1849]

Figure 4. Long Ditton waterworks. (D 23)

Cast-iron, with a very small acorn finial. A listed Grade
II monument.

22. Esher - parish pump. (TQ138645)
   This cast-iron pump was erected by the parish over the
public well, six feet in diameter and over thirty feet
deep, using the sum of £80 given to them by the Comte de
Paris, who lived in nearby Claremont, on the occasion of
his marriage in 1864. The pump was cast by Mr Dickie, at
a cost of £57 10s including a brass inscription plate.
Within twelve years the local sanitary authority declared
the water "unfit for Man or Beast" and the pump was
removed to Sandown Park racecourse. It was returned to
the village and re-erected on the village green in 1961
when the racecourse was modernised. Unfortunately the
large cast-iron trough was not re-erected with it. The
pump is exactly identical to the one in Hampton Court
Palace and must have been cast to the same pattern.

23. Long Ditton - Waterworks. (TQ172673)
   The Metropolis Water Act of 1852 prohibited the
extraction of water for household purposes from the
Thames below Teddington Weir. Even before this, however,
the Lambeth Water Company had decided to move its intake
upstream, and built works at Long Ditton, which were
completed and opened in the same year as the General Act
was passed. Another company - the Chelsea - quickly
followed suit and joined the Lambeth here. The two
establishments existed side by side until their
incorporation into the Metropolitan Water Board in 1903.
With the rationalisation made possible by that merger,
together with the move away from steam power to electric,
the amount of plant and buildings in use gradually
diminished and is now but a fraction of what it once was.

24. West Molesey - Waterworks and reservoirs. (TQ120667)
   Soon after the two water companies had moved to Long
Ditton (see previous paragraph), they much regretted their
choice of site, as, due to turbulence caused by outfalls
of the rivers Mole, Ember and Rythe, they sucked up a
great deal of mud with the water which was difficult and
expensive to filter out. In 1872, therefore, the Lambeth
moved its intake upstream to the cleaner waters of West
Molesey, and established storage reservoirs here. The
Chelsea, after an abortive attempt to build opposite
Hampton Court Palace, followed them three years later.
Both companies had pumping stations to lift the water from
the Thames into the reservoirs and concrete wharves on the
river bank to unload coal to power the steam engines. The
boiler houses and pumps have been demolished for some
years, but the wharves still remain by the river side, now
used only by overnight pleasure cruisers.

25. East Molesey - Island Barn Reservoir. (TQ138670)
   Authorized by the Lambeth Water Act of 1900, it was

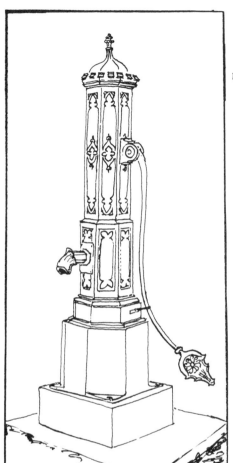

Figure 5. Esher parish pump.(D22)

Figure 6. Hersham electricity
kiosk,Byfleet Road. (D33)

completed by the Metropolitan Water Board, and opened in 1911, with a capacity of 992 million gallons, and covering some 121 acres.

26. Walton-on-Thames - Knights and Bessborough Reservoirs. (TQ120680)
    Started in 1898 on the site of the old mansion of Apps Court, by the Southwark and Vauxhall Water Company, whose works were across the river at Hampton and opened in 1907. The two have a combined water area of 125.5 acres and hold 1,198 million gallons.

27. Walton-on-Thames - Hurst Road Pumping and Filtration Station. (TQ115683)
    After the formation of the Metropolitan Water Board and the building of several new reservoirs in the vicinity, it was decided to concentrate all pumping requirements in one station in Hurst Road at Walton. The engines were started on 10 June 1911 by John Burns, President of the Local Government Board; on 19 July 1926 an extension was inaugurated by Neville Chamberlain, Minister of Health. Additional filter beds were opened in 1950. The steam engines which originally drove the pumps have now been replaced by electric power. An overhead ropeway ran from the boiler house to the coal wharf on the towpath. The wharf is still in existence.

28. Walton-on-Thames - Queen Elizabeth II Reservoir. (TQ120670)
    This reservoir, which holds 4,300 million gallons and covers 317 acres, was authorised by Act of Parliament in 1935. Construction was halted on the outbreak of war, and was not re-started until 1957. It was commissioned in 1962.

29. Walton-on-Thames - West Surrey Waterworks. (TQ087663)
    The West Surrey Water Company was incorporated in 1869 and an Act was passed to empower it to build works, to abstract water from the Thames, and to supply Walton and the surrounding area. Additional works were constructed under an Act of 1888. The pumphouses, one of which bears a stone with the date 1905, are built of yellow brick in typical 'waterworks' style. The original steam-driven beam engine has been replaced and the whole station considerably modernised.

30. Weybridge - Old Avenue water tower and reservoirs. (TQ085626)
    The original Act incorporating the West Surrey Water Company in 1869 also sanctioned the construction of a covered reservoir on the top of St George's Hill. In 1914 the company built a tall brick water tower by the side of this reservoir, but it was subsequently realised that they possessed no Parliamentary authority for this, and had exceeded their powers in so doing. To regularise the

matter and to give powers for an additional reservoir an
Act was passed in 1931. The reservoirs here now have a
combined capacity of six million gallons.

Gas.

31. Gas for the supply of the area originally came from
four separate sources - from the Hampton Court Gas
Company's works at Hampton Wick, the Kingston Gas Company,
the Cobham Gas and Coke Company, and the Walton and
Weybridge Gas Company.

Electricity.

There is now no public electricity supply generated within
Elmbridge, and the stations of all the local companies who
formerly provided power for the district have closed down.

32. Weybridge - former generating station. (TQ075654)
    The only building remaining from the old generating
stations exists in Church Walk at Weybridge. It was built
in 1890 by the Weybridge Electric Supply Company for
lighting the streets but closed after six years. Part has
been converted into four cottages and the rest is now used
as a furniture repository.

33. Hersham - Electricity kiosk, Byfleet Road, (TQ079611)
    This circular cast-iron kiosk originally housed a
transformer to boost the flagging voltage at the end of a
long supply feed. It was manufactured by the British
Electric Transformer Company of Hayes, Middlesex, probably
in the first decade of this century, and no doubt
incorporated a street lamp over the top at one time.

34. East Molesey - Substation, Feltham Avenue. (TQ153684)
    This corrugated iron building which is now used as an
electricity substation and workshop, was originally the
Trinity Church at New Malden. It was purchased,
dismantled, re-erected here, and opened as a public hall in
1882 and later transferred to its present use.

Telephones.

35. East Molesey - Former telephone call box. (TQ148679)
    This unusual small kiosk-like building jutting out from
the front of No. 44 Walton Road, East Molesey, now used as
a shop window for Colena Ladies Outfitters, was the first
public telephone call box in the district, opened in
October 1900.

Sewerage.

The sewerage and drainage systems within the Borough,
although considerably modernised, still rely to a great
degree on the schemes laid down by the separate local

sanitary authorities during Victoria's reign. The works now are:-

36. Cobham. (TQ100607)
    No filtration takes place here now, and the works consist only of pumps which transfer the untreated water to Esher for processing.

37. East Molesey. (TQ133674)
    Opened in 1894, but, like Cobham, the sewage is now pumped from here to Esher for treatment.

38. Esher. (TQ134663)
    Originally constructed in 1888/9 by the Kingston Rural Sanitary Authority to serve Esher and the Dittons, but since completely modernised and enlarged to take the water formerly treated at Cobham, Hersham, Molesey, and Walton.

39. Hersham. (TQ125657)
    Constructed at North Weylands Farm under an enabling Act of 1897 and commissioned in 1900. It is now closed down and the sewage is delivered to the Esher works on the other side of the Mole.

40. Walton. (TQ109678)
    Originally started by the Walton Vestry on land near Apps Court, where the sewage was simply poured over the surrounding farm land. Improvements were made over the years, but after 1950 the plant was progressively closed down and the water was pumped firstly to Hersham and then to Esher for treatment.

41. Weybridge - Seven Arches Treatment Works. (TQ068632)
    Opened in 1973 by the Walton and Weybridge Urban District Council, to replace the old works within the perimeter of Brooklands Track on the opposite side of the railway, which also treated sewage pumped from a station in Walton Lane.

E. TRAVEL.

Railways.

The London to Southampton Railway was authorized by Act of Parliament in 1834 and opened as far as Woking on 21 May 1838. The stations within Elmbridge are :-

42. Esher. (TQ147658)   Both of these stations are
43. Walton-on-Thames (TQ105649) on their original sites,
                             but were enlarged when the
                             station was four-tracked.

44. Weybridge. (TQ074636)
    This station was rebuilt on a new site about a mile further down the line in 1857.

45. Hersham. (TQ122654)
    Opened on 28 September 1936 to serve a rapidly expanding
area.
    Two spurs from the main line were sanctioned in 1844. A
branch from Weybridge to Chertsey, which has no stations
within the Borough; and a branch from Surbiton to Hampton
Court (East Molesey), which has two stations:-

46. Thames Ditton. (TQ157668)   Both opened on 2 February
47. Hampton Court. (TQ154673)   1849.

48. Hampton Court Junction flyover. (TQ162662)
    This is a steel girder viaduct with long brick-arch
approaches, constructed in 1913/4, to obviate the necessity
of Hampton Court trains standing by waiting for other
trains to clear before passing over the main line tracks.

A line from Surbiton, via Cobham to Guildford, for long
just known as "The New Line", was opened on 2 February
1885. The stations on this line within Elmbridge are:-

49. Claygate. (TQ151637)   All original stations dating from
50. Oxshott.   (TQ142609)   when the line was opened, but
51. Cobham.   (TQ123589)   altered slightly from time to
                            time.

52. Hinchley Wood. (TQ156653)
    Opened on 20 October 1930, to serve the building estates
ribbon developed along the newly opened Kingston By-Pass.

Roads.

The most important historical road to run through the
Borough is undoubtedly the A3 Portsmouth Road, now
by-passed for much of its old route. It was first brought
under the control of a turn-pike trust by Act of Parliament
in 1772, the terms of which were later amended by
subsequent legislation. A series of triangular-shaped
milestones were placed along its length, probably in the
late eighteenth century, giving the distances from Hyde
Park Corner, Portsmouth, and the nearest villages on either
side. The sites are, or were, as follows (the miles quoted
are those from Hyde Park Corner):-

53. 11 miles. (TQ172673)
    North side of road, near Long Ditton/Kingston boundary.
Now missing.

54. 12 miles. (TQ161663)
    North side of the road, near Hampton Court branch
railway bridge. Now missing.

55. 13 miles. (TQ146656)
    North side of road, near the "Orleans Arms". Now
missing.

18

56. 14 miles. (TQ136642)
   South side of road, opposite Hill House.   Now missing.

57. 15 miles. (TQ126629)
   South side of road, south of Horseshoe Clump.

58. 16 miles. (TQ117616)
   South side of road, opposite junction with Fairmile
Lane.

59. 17 miles. (TQ106605)
   South side of road, opposite Seven Hills Motel.   This
stone disappeared during recent dualling of road.

All the stones indicated as missing are shown on 6 in.
O.S. maps up to the provisional edition of 1938.
   Besides these, there are a number of square-cut stones
to the south of the Portsmouth Road which probably
indicated a way used by coachmen by-passing Esher and
Stoney Hill.   Some of these are dated 1747 and are
distanced from Cornhill; some are dated 1768 and distanced
from Westminster Bridge; some have both dates and
distances.   They are now situated as follows:-

61. Littleworth Road. (TQ151652)
   West side of road, halfway between Portsmouth Road and
Oaken Lane.

62. Milbourne Lane. (TQ144641)
   South side of road, between Nos. 24 and 26.

63. Broom Close. (TQ138643)
   Outside a house called "Milestone".   This stone was
moved some years ago from the east side of Claremont Lane
(TQ140643).

64. In Claremont Park. (TQ134629)
   This stone is also distanced to Newcastle House, the
London home of the Duke of Newcastle, owner of Claremont
in the seventeenth century, and is included in the
schedule of Ancient Monuments.

65. Portsmouth Road. (TQ117615)
   North side of road, outside Fairmile Hotel.

66. Hill House Farm. (TQ135640)
   In private grounds off the north side of Portsmouth
Road.   This listed Ancient Monument is impossible to see
as the grounds are overgrown.   It was probably moved here
from elsewhere to serve as a garden ornament.

67. Portsmouth Road - "The White Lady". (TQ146656)
   A listed Ancient Monument, standing outside the "Orleans
Arms" by the junction of Station Road. It stands about
eight feet high, surmounted by a ball finial bearing the
date 1767. It was probably erected by the owners of
Hampton Court Bridge to encourage travellers to use the
bridge in preference to the turn-pike. It was renovated in
1848 when it was suggested that it may have been
constructed of redundant mill stones.

   The road leading from Thames Ditton to Ewell was
turnpiked by Act in 1755. Only one milestone exists within
the Borough:-

68. Long Ditton - Ewell Road. (TQ168665)
   On west side of road by junction of Orchard Close. A
square-cut stone about three feet high, distanced 5 1/4
miles to Ewell.

Horse and cattle troughs.

69. Claygate. (TQ156636)
   Outside the "Hare and Hounds". Erected in 1911 for the
Coronation of King George V.

70. East Molesey. (TQ151683)
   At the junction of Bridge and Wolsey Roads.
Incorporated into a tall marble drinking fountain, and
erected for the Jubilee of Queen Victoria.

71. Thames Ditton. (TQ161671)
   On the roundabout at the junction of High Street and St
Leonards Road. Two troughs incorporated into a group with
a drinking fountain, and erected by a lord of the manor in
1879.

72. Walton-on-Thames. (TQ100649)
   At the junction of Ashley and Station Roads. In the
summer the bowl is resplendent with colourful flowers, a
delightful way to utilise these once useful but now mostly
redundant pieces of street furniture.

73. Weybridge. (TQ075637)
   On the east side of Heath Road, outside the "Hand and
Spear".

Rivers.

River Thames, once a very important navigational highway:-

74. Shepperton Lock. (TQ074659)
75. Sunbury Lock. (TQ114688) ·
These were erected under an Act of Parliament of
1810 to improve the navigation of the Thames. The original
lock-keeper's house for Sunbury Lock still stands by the

Figure 7. Esher - Portsmouth Road.
"The White Lady" milestone. (E 67)

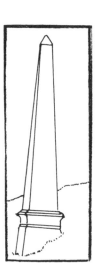
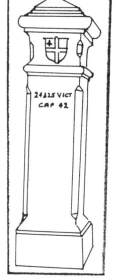

Figure 8. City of London tax posts.
From the left : - types a,b,c,d. (F 88 - 111)

towpath at Walton-on-Thames.

76. Molesey Lock. (TQ151687)
   Authorised under an amending Act of 1812, but not opened
until 1815.

77. Weybridge - D'Oyley Carte Island Bridge. (TQ077659)
   An elegant single span bridge, with very high arch.
Built in 1964, of a single steel box girder with treads, to
connect Eyot House, formerly the home of Rupert D'Oyley
Carte, with the mainland.

78. Walton Bridge. (TQ093665)
   Four different bridges have at times spanned the river
here. The first, opened in 1750, was built of wood in
three arches, with smaller arches leading to it; the
second was of brick and stone in four arches, opened in
1786; this collapsed in August 1859 and was replaced by a
wrought-iron girder structure, designed by E.T. Murray.
This suffered badly by war time bomb damage and in 1953 was
declared unsafe. As a 'temporary' measure, it was
by-passed by a "Callender- Hamilton" type bridge which is
still used. The third bridge stood as a rusting hulk for
many years and was finally dismantled in 1985.

79. Hampton Court Bridge. (TQ154685)
   There have also been four bridges at this point. The
first, of timber in seven arches, opened in 1753; the
second, also of timber in eleven arches, in 1778; the
third, of wrought-iron girders on cast-iron columns in five
arches, in 1865; the fourth,of ferro-concrete with brick
and stone facings, designed by Sir Edwin Lutyens, opened in
1933. This is a Grade II listed monument.

River Ember.

80. East Molesey - Hampton Court Way Bridge. (TQ154682)
   The construction of Hampton Court Way in 1933 to link
the new Hampton Court Bridge to the Portsmouth Road,
necessitated the spanning of the River Ember. This
structure, too, was designed by Sir Edwin Lutyens in the
same style and using the same materials as the main bridge.
It is seen to best advantage either from the railway
station or the forecourt of the adjacent petrol station.
Also a listed Grade II monument.

Rivers Mole and Ember.

81. East Molesey - Esher Road Bridges. (TQ149677)
   The present Esher Road was constructed in the
mid-eighteenth century as an approach to Hampton Court
Bridge, the owner of which built two wooden bridges to span
the Mole and Ember, and maintained them until 1876 when the
tolls ceased. They were replaced by wrought-iron girder
bridges in the 1880's. That over the Ember was demolished

in 1985 as part of the flood prevention scheme, and was
replaced by a concrete structure.

River Mole.

82. Albany Bridge. (TQ130645)
   This bridge, which was named after the Duchess of Albany
who lived in nearby Claremont, connects Esher to Hersham.
An ornamental timber bridge, thought to have been built
early in Victoria's reign, was replaced by a stone parapet
bridge in 1907. The present elegant, concrete bridge,
opened in 1965, is best seen from the nearby recreation
ground.

83. Cobham Bridge. (TQ099605)
   It is thought that there has been a bridge on this site
from at least the twelfth century, as a plaque on the
present bridge indicates. Up to 1782 it was a wooden
bridge, the upkeep of which was the liability of the lords
of the adjacent manors. In that year an Act was passed for
the county authorities to take over responsibility, and
their surveyor, George Gwilt, designed and constructed the
now existing bridge, which was widened in 1914. It is a
listed Grade II monument.

84. Downside Bridge. (TQ107595)
   This bridge, like Cobham, was a medieval foundation, and
was also re-built in 1786 by Gwilt in a similar style.
During the catastrophic floods of September 1968, the
centre arches were entirely washed away. A temporary steel
girder bridge was erected across the broken spans and used
until the present bridge was opened in 1971.

River Wey.

85. Weybridge Bridge. (TQ068647)
   The original bridge, after which the town was named,
existed at the end of Bridge Street on the road to
Chertsey. An old timber structure was replaced by another
of the same material in 1808. The present three-arched
bridge of steel girders on brick and stone faced piers and
abutments with cast-iron balustrades, was opened in 1865.
A new road and bridge, by-passing the old road, was begun
in 1939 but not completed until after the War had finished.

Canals.

86. Wey Navigation - Thames Lock. (TQ073655)
   The River Wey was canalised and made navigable under an
Act passed in 1651, and opened for use two years later. It
is said to have been the first navigation in this country
to utilise pound locks. The last commercial barges ran in
1958, after which the whole canal was handed over to the
National Trust. The only lock within Elmbridge Borough,
known as "Thames Lock", was constructed just above the

confluence with the River Thames.   The lock-keeper's
cottage still stands.

87. River Thames - Desborough Channel. (TQ085660)
   A canal by-passing the long loop of the river between
Weybridge and Walton was proposed as early as 1816, but was
frustrated by various interests.   It was, in fact, over a
century later in 1930 that work started on the cut.   It was
opened on 10 July 1935 by Lord Desborough, Chairman of the
Thames Conservancy, and is one hundred feet wide and three
quarters of a mile in length, necessitating the excavation
and removal of some 800,000 cubic yards of material.   At
each end, bridges of steel girders on stone piers and
abutments carry the road and the mains from the water works
across the canal.

F.MISCELLANEOUS.

City of London Coal and Wine Posts.

These were erected under Acts of Parliament passed
respectively in 1851 and 1861, and continued the tax on
coal and wine coming into the Metropolis.   The earlier Act
defined the area of taxation as that within twenty miles of
the General Post Office, the later one reduced it to the
Metropolitan Police District, which cuts across the present
Elmbridge Borough.   There are four different types of post
to be seen in the area, viz:-

a). A stubby granite pillar, marked for the 1851 Act,
    intended for towing paths;

b). A tall slender granite obelisk for use by railway
    lines, also for the earlier Act;

c). Cast-iron pillars about four feet high, marked with the
    1861 Act, for roadside use;

d). Cast-iron obelisks, much shorter than type b, for
    railways.

All display the arms of the City of London and the
reference of the Act under which they were erected.   Some
have long since disappeared.   Those still existing in the
Borough are sited as follows.   (All type c unless stated
otherwise):-

88. On the Thames towpath, east bank of river, a quarter
    mile north of the junction of the Desborough Channel.
    (TQ079664)

89. On the Thames towpath, south bank of river, 300 yards
    east of No.88. (TQ082664)

90. In a field south of Walton Lane, quarter mile
    south-west of Walton Bridge. (TQ091661)

91. North-west side of the approach to Walton Bridge.
    (TQ095664)

92. North-east end of Sunbury Lock Ait. (TQ109685)

93. On the Thames towpath, south bank of river, at
    Walton/West Molesey boundary. (TQ116687). Type a. This
    was placed here in 1861, probably from the Wey
    Navigation at Byfleet.

94. North side of Hurst Road, at Walton/West Molesey
    boundary. (TQ122685)

95. South-west corner of junction of Walton and Molesey
    Roads. (TQ124679)

96. East side of Molesey Road, at Walton/West Molesey
    boundary. (TQ125675)

97. North side of River Ember, at East Molesey/Esher/Walton
    boundary. (TQ140658). No public access to site. This
    post fell into the river during the 1968 floods but was
    rescued and reinstated after representations by the
    Esher District Local History Society.

98. North side of railway embankment by Douglas Road at
    Esher/Thames Ditton boundary. (TQ139658). Type b. Moved
    here in 1861 from Weybridge, further down the line.

99. South side of Lower Green Road. (TQ138657). This has
    been moved about one hundred yards from its original
    position.

100. North side of Portsmouth Road, by "Old Toll House".
    (TQ145654)

101. West side of Littleworth Road, outside "Lessworth".
    (TQ147647)

102. North-west corner of junction of Littleworth and New
    Roads. (TQ147645)

103. South-west corner of junction of Milbourne and Arbrook
    Lanes. (TQ145641)

104. West side of Arbrook Farm Road, by River Rythe Bridge.
    (TQ143628)

105. West side of Copsem Lane, just south of A3 roundabout.
    (TQ140623)

106. North-west corner of junction of Copsem and Sandy

Lanes. (TQ140617)
107. East side of railway cutting, about fifty yards south of Stokesheath Road bridge. (TQ148618). Type d.

108. South side of Stokesheath Road, in the garden of "Foxholes". (TQ148618)

109. On Stokesheath Farm. (TQ151617). No public access to site.

110. South side of Birchwood Lane. (TQ154620)

111. East side of New Road. (TQ158625)

Telegraph Towers.

The revised signalling route between the Admiralty in London and Portsmouth Dockyard laid down in 1820/2, using a semaphore system devised by Admiral Sir Home Riggs Popham, passed through two stations in the Borough, both of which survive. The system was in use until 1847.

112. Hinchley Wood. (TQ158648)
A three storeyed-brick building, externally stuccoed. Has been used until recently as a private building. Locally listed as a building of historical interest.

113. Chatley Heath. (TQ088587)
A massive octagonal citadel, five storeys and sixty feet high, surmounted by a parapet built of red brick, plastered over with cement which has badly peeled off in places. Although in an extremely remote position, it was occupied as a residence until 1963, when it was condemned as unfit because of lack of services, since when it has been badly vandalised and was partly damaged by fire in 1984. The tower has been restored by Surrey County Council and the Surrey Historic Buildings Trust to mark the centenary of the County Council with accommodation for a resident warden, a museum and the restored signalling apparatus. A scheduled Ancient Monument.

Water.

114. Esher - Claremont horse pump. (TQ129624)
On Esher Common, near the north bank of Black Pond, may just be traced the remains of what was once a horse or donkey operated pump. Originally housed in a circular brick and tiled building with a louvred finial, which destroyed during the First World War, it was constructed to supply water from the springs hereabouts, which was first collected into reservoirs (still in existence and forming delightfully secluded ponds) and then pumped through pipes to the mansion of Claremont. The pipes were originally of lead, but after this had caused some illness they were replaced by pipes of iron.

Figure 9. Chatley Heath semaphore tower. (F 113)

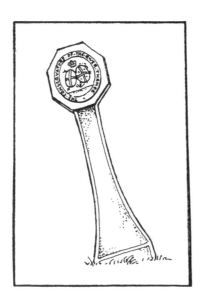

Figure 10. Thames Conservancy boundary marker. (F 158)

Figure 11. Water mains wayleave marker. (F 159)

115. Painshill - Water wheel and pump house. (TQ129624)
    The landscaped park of Painshill was laid out by Charles
Hamilton in the late eighteenth century. It includes a
nineteen acre lake, which as it stands higher than the
adjacent River Mole, had first to be filled and kept topped
up by lifting water from the lower level. There have been
three devices mentioned for raising water from the river to
the lake, a lift of about twelve feet. The first a wheel,
thirty-six feet in diameter, with paddles around its
circumference, turned by the flow of the stream, and with
four leather tubes curved to the axis, which scooped up the
water and delivered it to the middle where it flowed out of
a trough and so into the lake. The second is depicted in
an illustration which appeared in the Gentleman's Magazine
in 1771, and shows an endless chain of buckets worked by a
cog and pinion from a shaft rotated by a horse. This was
replaced in the 1830's by a pump operated by a large
cast-iron water wheel, thirty feet in diameter, which like
the first, worked by the flow of the river. It was made by
the firm of Bramah and Son. The whole structure has been
terribly dilapidated, the wooden weather-boarded pumphouse
falling to pieces, the water wheel shedding its paddles and
the pumps and connecting rods rusting up. However, this
listed Grade II monument has now been restored to its
former glory.

116. Painshill - Water supply pump. (TQ095601)
    This pump, situated near the Bath-house and worked by
horse power, was originally installed to supply water to
the house from a nearby spring. It is now being restored.

117. Cobham - Water wheel. (TQ114589)
    A small water wheel in Cobham Park, installed in 1884 to
pump water from the River Mole to the house, by Whitmore
and Binyon of Suffolk. The only recorded wheel by this
firm in Surrey. The wheel is on private land.

118. Oxshott - Jessop's Well. (TQ159611)
    In a remote part of Prince's Coverts on what was once
Stoke Common stands a small square brick and tiled pump
house. It bears a stone panel with the words JESSOP'S
WELL. This little building, erected in the eighteenth
century, stands over a mineral spa, the waters of which
exhibited extreme purgative qualities. It is said that a
man who stood in the water bare-legged for three hours to
clean the well out was purged for a week. At one time the
water was supposed to ooze out of the spring at a rate of
one hundred and sixty gallons a day and bottles of the
stuff were taken to be sold in London. To prove that
graffiti are not just twentieth century phenomena, some of
the initials carved into the soft red brick date back to
1778.

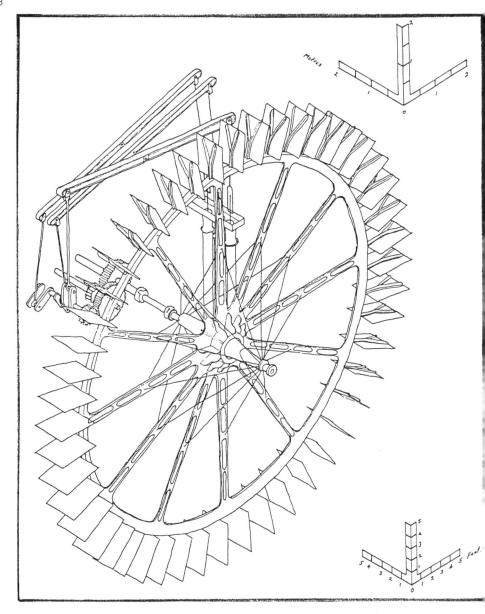

Figure 12. Painshill Park, Cobham.
Water wheel and pumps. (F 115)

Fire Engine Houses.

The following buildings were once village fire stations,
but are now no longer used for that purpose.

119. Cobham - The Tilt. (TQ114597)
   Originally built about 1833 as a parish school and later
used to house the Merryweather steam fire engine donated to
the village by Mr Charles Combe of Cobham Park in 1889. Now
used by a car hire firm.

120. East Molesey - 92 Walton Road. (TQ146680)
   Built in 1900 to the design of Mr John Stevenson,
surveyor to the Molesey Urban District Council. It was
closed as a fire station in 1961, and is now used by the St
John's Ambulance Brigade.

121. Esher - The Green. (TQ138649)
   Built in the 1890's on a piece of ground provided by
Sandown Park Racing Club, for which the Brigade paid a rent
of one shilling a year. In 1930 the engine was moved to a
new station by the side of the council offices in
Portsmouth Road, and the old premises were adapted as
a private dwelling.

Figure 13. Oxshott.
Jessop's Well. (F 118)

Cinemas.

122. Esher - The Embassy. (TQ140648)
    The only cinema still operating as such within the
Borough. Purpose built in the flamboyant picture house
style of the 1930's.

The following buildings used at the height of the cinema
boom still stand but are no longer used as such :-

123. Cobham - Village Hall. (TQ108601)
    The Village Hall in Anyards Road, built by public
subscription in 1888, was used as a cinema during the
1930's.

124. East Molesey - 62 Bridge Road. (TQ153682)
    A purpose built cinema, opened in 1912 as the "East
Molesey and Hampton Court Picture Hall", it was purchased
by one of the cinema chains in 1932, modernised and
re-named "The Court Cinema". It closed in 1937 and the
premises were taken over as a printing works.

125. Walton-on-Thames - 19 Church Street. (TQ101665)
    An early purpose built cinema called "The Regent", now
used as a showroom by a firm of house furnishers.

126. Weybridge - Weybridge Hall. (TQ072648)
    This stands on the corner of Church Street and Minorca
Road. It was opened as "Weybridge Kinema Theatre" in
1920, later to become "King George's" and then "The
County". It closed its doors in the early 50's and the
building was acquired by the local authority for a public
hall.

127. Weybridge - Queens Road. (TQ083645)
    A purpose built cinema erected by the Odeon chain in
1934 and closed in 1960. It is now used as a Roman
Catholic church, known as St Martin de Porres.

Letter Boxes.

Victorian letter boxes still stand at the following
places:-

128. Cobham - Plough Lane. (TQ107593)
    Wall letter box, south side of road, near junction with
Downside Road.

129. Cobham - Tilt Road. (TQ114597)
    Wall letter box, south-west side of road, on the side
of the former fire station. (See No. 119 above).

130. Cobham - Tilt Road. (TQ115594)
    Wall letter box in a square brick pillar, south-west
side of road, outside no. 83.

131. Walton-on-Thames - Queens Road. (TQ090641)
    Pillar box, north side of road, about fifty yards west
of junction with Common Road.   This box, which was cast by
Handyside and Co. Ltd., of Derby and London between 1883
and 1887, has no royal cipher nor the letters POST OFFICE.
(See S.I.H.G. Newletter No. 25, February 1985,p.12.)

The following are pillar boxes cast by Handyside and Co.
between 1887 and 1901 and have an intertwined VR monogram:-

132. Esher - High Street. (TQ140648)
    South-west side of road, outside No.21 (Boots the
Chemist).

133. Hersham - Mayfield Road. (TQ107648)
    North side of road, opposite junction with Woodside
Avenue.

134. Oatlands - Oatlands Avenue. (TQ086643)
    South side of road, opposite junction with Oatlands
Close.

135. Thames Ditton - Weston Green Road. (TQ154666)
    West side of road, near "The Harrow".

136. Walton-on-Thames - Hersham Road. (TQ105657)
    North-east side of road, by junction with Crutchfield
Lane.

137. West Molesey - Hurst Road. (TQ131687)
    North side of road, by junction with Cherry Orchard
Road.

138. Weybridge - Church Street. (TQ072648)
    North side of road, by junction with Minorca Road.

Besides those mentioned above, a Victorian pillar box,
formerly sited in Manor Road, Walton-on-Thames, is now
preserved and on display in Weybridge Museum.

During the brief and dramatic reign of Edward VIII in 1936,
only about one hundred and thirty post boxes bearing his
royal cipher were erected by the Post Office.   Of this
number, six are to be found within the Elmbridge Borough,
all pillar boxes:-

139. Claygate - Stevens Lane. (TQ163663)
    North-east corner of junction with Ruxley Ridge.

140. Esher - Blackhills. (TQ130627)
    South side of road about five hundred yards from
Portsmouth Road.

141. Esher - Portsmouth Road. (TQ137644)
    East side of road, opposite Moore Place Hotel.

142. Hersham - Mayfield Road. (TQ102648)
   West side of road opposite Fenner House. This box
first stood in Queens Road opposite junction with Burwood
Park Road.

143. Thames Ditton - Portsmouth Road. (TQ150656)
   Near the Scilly Isles roundabout.

144. Thames Ditton - Littleworth Road. (TQ148644)
   East side of road, opposite junction with New Road.

Icehouses.

The following icehouses still remain. All are on private
ground, with restricted or no public access:-

145. Cobham - Cobham Park. (TQ111592)
   No details known.

146. Cobham - Painshill Park. (TQ097601)
   A very well preserved brick domed structure covered
with soil.

147. Cobham - Pyports. (TQ107598)
   A brick structure, bearing the inscription "GP1765".

148. East Molesey - 12 Beauchamp Road, (TQ143678)
   A domed brick building, now used as a garden shed.
Formerly served East Molesey Park.

149. Esher - Claremont. (TQ132634)
   In the grounds of the park, now much vandalised.

150. Hersham - Burwood House. (TQ097617)
   A massive structure in good state of preservation.

151. Hersham - Burwood Park. (TQ103637)
   The entrance is now blocked up with brick and concrete.

152. Walton-on-Thames - Manor Road. (TQ099699)
   Formerly in the grounds of Mount Felix, now in the
garden of a private house, but little remains.

153. Walton-on-Thames - Silverdale Avenue. (TQ095655)
   An eighteenth century structure, originally serving
Ashley Park, now in the garden of a private house.

Slaughter house.

154. Thames Ditton - High Street.(TQ160669)
   On west side of road, a seventeenth century timber
building.   A listed Grade II monument, now used as a
picture gallery.

155. East Molesey/West Molesey - Walton Road. (TQ139686)
   On north side of road, opposite junction with Avern
Road. A small stone marked EM and WM. Erected in 1865, on
the last occasion of the perambulation of the parish
bounds. During road works some years ago, the stone was
re-erected about twenty yards westward of the true
boundary.

156. Walton-on-Thames/ Weybridge boundary.
   A number of stones were placed along the boundary
between the two parishes in 1802. One of these
still survives in the recreation ground at Oatlands.
(TQ085648)

157. City of London Wall Posts. (TQ097667)
   Along the towing path between Walton Wharf and Walton
Bridge appear a number of cast iron posts bearing the
shield of the arms of the Corporation of the City of
London. The Corporation was, of course, responsible for
the navigation of the Thames before 1857. It is not
certain whether these were erected to define the boundary
of the Corporation's rights or just as stanchions to
support the retaining wall of the neighbouring property
which stands higher than the towing path.

158. Thames Conservancy Boundary Marks.
   A number of markers may be seen at various places along
the towing path to delineate the jurisdiction of the
Thames Conservators, who took over responsibility for the
river from the City of London. Made of cast-iron with the
badge of the Conservators displayed on an octagonal head.
One of the most accessible can be found near Walton Bridge
by the fence of Walton Marine Chandlery (TQ095675).
Another is in a field by the towing path at Weybridge
(TQ082664).

159. Water mains wayleave markers.
   Access to the water authority's main pipelines, those
leading from the pumping stations to the reservoirs and
filtration works, is required at all times. Therefore,
where these diverge from the public highways and cross
private land, the authority has a wayleave prohibiting
building and providing facility to dig up and repair the
pipes when necessary. Cast-iron markers are placed at
certain spots to distinguish their path. They date from
various years depending on when the mains were laid.
Examples as follows:- In the front garden of No.37 Down
Street, West Molesey (two different types)(TQ133679); On
the bank of the River Rythe adjacent to Winters Bridge,
Long Ditton (Lambeth Water Company) (TQ166669); Behind the
Library in Mercer Close, Thames Ditton (Metropolitan Water
Board) (TQ160666).

160. Oil pipe line markers.
    Early in the Second World War, to save oil tankers from
the hazardous trip up the English Channel to London, a
pipe line was constructed from Avonmouth Docks to storage
tanks near the towing path at Walton-on-Thames (TQ104676),
from which the fuel was transferred to barges for the
final distribution to the Metropolis. Later a further
line was laid to the coast and on to the Continent to
supply our invading armies (code name PLUTO). Later still
in 1959 a further branch was constructed to Heathrow
Airport. Markers are laid along the line of these pipes
to distinguish their path. Two of the most accessible
appear along the towing path at Walton, just westward of
the Anglers Hotel (TQ097667). These are of cast concrete
about eighteen inches high bearing the letters MPL
(Ministry pipe line).

Bronze castings.

At one time a quite famous bronze foundry was situated in
Summer Road, Thames Ditton. Started in 1874, it is
believed to have been the only building purpose-built
specifically for the casting of statues and ecclesiastical
bronze work. Many celebrated monuments were produced in
these small works and far and wide are the places to which
they were sent. A list of the known Thames Ditton cast
statues would include most countries of the Commonwealth
and many others as well. The copy of 'Eros' for
Piccadilly, Manchester, was produced here and so too was
the massive "Peace" Quadriga above the Wellington Arch on
Constitution Hill, thirty-two feet high and twenty-eight
tons, which took three and a half years to cast. Founding
ceased here in 1940 and the buildings were demolished in
1972. An 1874 gantry crane which spanned the whole
production area, was, however, saved by Surrey Industrial
History Group and is on display at the Old Kiln Museum,
Tilford. Examples of the work carried out in the foundry
may be seen in the Borough at the following places:-

161. Esher - High Street. (TQ138645)
    North side of road, on The Green. Statue of Britannia
on the Diamond Jubilee Memorial, 1897. Sculpted by F.J.
Williamson.

162. Oxshott - Blundell Lane. (TQ132596)
    At the Polyapes Scouts Camping Ground. A statue of a
scout in uniform, erected as a memorial to all scouts who
perished in the First World War; unveiled in 1929.
Sculpted by Samuel Ward Willis.

163. Thames Ditton - St Nicholas Church. (TQ161673)
    War memorial.

164. Thames Ditton - Churchyard. (TQ161673)
    Inscribed scroll on gravestone to Alfred Morrison
(d.1924), formerly foreman moulder in the foundry.

Cast-iron grave markers.

165. In an area such as Elmbridge, which has no natural
deposits of stone, alternative materials for marking graves
were often sought. In the past this was usually timber,
which rapidly deteriorated. A number of cast-iron
memorials may be seen. However, the disadvantage of this
was the inability to add further names once the monument
had been cast. An ingenious method for overcoming this
problem can be seen in St Nicholas churchyard at Thames
Ditton (TQ161673), where one cast-iron memorial, cast in
1897, has four lead panels inserted, the soft metal of
which could quite easily be stamped with the names of later
interments.

Wrought-iron work.

166. Thames Ditton - Watts Road. (TQ161667)
    On the west side of the road, in front of Basing House,
an early eighteenth century entrance gate and gateway, with
an interesting peripatetic history. They were erected here
when the house was built in the early 1920's and came from
Cheam where they then formed an entrance to the kitchen
garden of Cheam House, having previously graced the main
entrance to the mansion. Before this they are thought to
have been either at Nonsuch Palace or West Cheam Manor
House. A locally listed ancient monument.

Figure 14. Weybridge.
Old Avenue water tower. (D 30)

BROOKLANDS RACE TRACK

Brooklands was the world's first purpose-built banked race track. It was built as the result of the national pride of Hugh Locke King who as a keen pioneer motorist, decided that Britain should have a track on which the country's growing motor industry could test and develop its products despite the restrictive legislation on our roads in the first decade of this century. Foreign manufacturers had already gained tremendous sales advantages by winning the inter-continental road races and reaping the benefits of good publicity.

The construction of Brooklands by primitive means was, at the time, regarded as the eighth wonder of the world. The decision to start was made in October 1906 and plans were drawn up for a roughly pear-shaped track of concrete, 100 feet wide, over two and a half miles around and with a finishing straight of over half a mile. The design called for clearing some 365 acres of Locke King's Weybridge estates either side of the River Wey, diversion of the river in three places, cutting through a natural hill, removing and re-siting 300,000 cubic yards of earth to make up two enormous bankings, collecting and mixing 200,000 tons of Portland cement, building two tunnels, three bridges, including one which carried the banked track over the river incorporating an early type of ferro-concrete construction, grandstands for 30,000 and spectator facilities for another 250,000, access roads, restaurants and an impressive clubhouse. It involved building a seven-mile branch railway line, purchasing 10 steam grabs and a steam navvy, six traction engines and a large number of horses and carts and some 2,000 shovels for the navvies brought in for the job. The time taken for all this was incredibly just nine months at a cost to Locke King of £150,000.

Shortly after the Track was constructed, Brooklands' open expanse began to attract pioneer aviators. It was here, in 1908, that A.V. Roe flew himself into the record books as the first Briton to fly a heavier than air machine of his own design, the Roe 1 Biplane. Others including Tommy Sopwith and Harry Hawker soon followed.

A 'flying village' gradually formed and flying schools opened, run by companies such as Sopwith, Bristol and Vickers. An embryonic aircraft industry developed rapidly and, during the First World War, Brooklands became Britain's largest aircraft manufacturing centre producing such legendary types as the Sopwith Camel and Vickers Gunbus biplanes.

During the 1920s and 30s a unique atmosphere was created for tens of thousands who watched motor car, motorcycle and even bicycle racing at Brooklands. Many notable engineers set up workshops and, in the case of Parry Thomas, even homes within the circuit.

On the death of Locke King in 1926, ownership of the Brooklands Estate passed to his widow who sold the track ten years later to Brooklands [Weybridge] Ltd. A new road circuit was opened in 1937 named after Sir Malcolm Campbell.

Brooklands bred a number of national and international heroes. John Cobb, Henry Segrave, George Eyston, Raymond Mays, Prince Bira of Siam, Kaye Don, Parry Thomas, Kay Petre, Tim Birkin and Malcolm Campbell amongst many others became household names.

Chosen as the starting and finishing point of the Daily Mail Round Britain Air Race in 1910, with a prize of £10,000, Brooklands' popularity as a venue for sporting and social events grew apace during the 1920s and 1930s. The Brooklands Aero Club subsequently formed in 1930 and its innovative Clubhouse, an early design by airport architect Graham Dawbarn opened two years later.

Brooklands also remained at the forefront of aviation design and development after the First World War with the production of the Vickers Vimy [which made the first non-stop transatlantic crossing in 1919] the Hawker Hurricane fighter and the Vickers Wellington bomber being best known.

The outbreak of the Second World War and subsequent permanent closure of the motor racing circuit in 1939 by no means sounded a death knell for Brooklands, although the motoring fraternity was later stunned by the news that the cost of restoring the Track post-war was prohibitive. Vickers-Armstrongs purchased the entire site in January 1946.

Aircraft production had stepped up at Brooklands during the war years - particularly over 2,500 Wellingtons assembled and test flown from the Vickers factory.

Post-war, Brooklands carried on its tradition of innovation in design and development and, under the direction of Barnes Wallis, the vast unique 'Stratosphere Chamber' was built in 1947 to explore the problems of pressurisation and climatic conditions on aircraft.

Vickers-Armstrongs meanwhile embarked on the design and manufacture of a new generation of aircraft and its successful family of civil airliners included the Viking, Viscount and VC10. Brooklands also had its part to play in the production of the BAC One-Eleven and Concorde.

Today the Brooklands Museum Trust is committed to ensuring the continuation of the Brooklands story and is currently developing a major project on 30 acres of the original site of so many milestone achievements and of so much excitement and endeavour.

AVIATION & MOTORING ACHIEVEMENTS AT BROOKLANDS

17 June 1907	Opening of Brooklands Motor Course - the World's first purpose-built motor-racing circuit.
28/29 June 1907	S.F. Edge sets up a 1,581 mile 24 hour endurance record.
8 June 1908	A.V. Roe made first powered flight in Britain.
20 April 1908	First official motorcycle race held.
May 1908	First women's motor race.
29 October 1909	Louis Paulhan made the first public flight in Britain in a Henry Farman Biplane.
1910	First woman pilots' licence gained by Mrs. Hilda Hewlett.
1911	World's first flight ticket office.
1911 & 1912	Marconi's early wireless experiments.
14 February 1913	Percy Lambert, driving a 25 hp, 4.5 litre, Talbot set up a new World Speed Record covering 103.84 miles in an hour.
25 September 1913	Adolph Pegoud became the first man to loop-the-loop in Britain flying a Bleriot monoplane.
August 1914	Brooklands had now issued the highest number of pilots' licences anywhere in Britain.
18 March 1915	Vickers Aviation began aircraft assembly at Brooklands - aircraft production continued on the same site until 1987.
15 June 1919	A Brooklands-built Vickers Vimy flown by Alcock and Brown made the first non-stop Transatlantic flight.
10 December 1919	A Brooklands-built Vickers Vimy made the first flight from England to Australia piloted by Ross and Keith Smith.
28 April 1921	Douglas Davidson became the first rider to exceed 100 mph in Britain, riding a Harley-Davidson.
17 May 1922	Kenelm Lee Guinness driving a V12 Sunbeam set the second and last World Land Speed Record established at Brooklands - 137.15 mph over one kilometre.

8 August 1926	First British Grand Prix held at Brooklands.
1932	R.G.J. Nash fastest time ever up Test Hill [7.45 seconds at 32.44mph].
1932	World aeroplane height record 43,976 ft. in a Brooklands-built Vickers Vespa.
27 October 1933	World Speed Record for a diesel-engined car taken by George Eyston at 104.86mph.
7 October 1935	John Cobb, driving the 24-litre Napier Railton set the ultimate Brooklands Lap Record of 143.44 mph and the highest speed recorded on the Track at 151.97 mph.
5 November 1935	First flight of the prototype Hawker Hurricane fighter from Brooklands.
1936	First aircraft to be fitted with an automatic pilot, a Brooklands-built Vickers Virginia.
15 June 1936	First flight of the Vickers B.9/32 - forerunner of the Wellington bomber.
7 November 1938	World long distance record of 7,157.7 miles set by Vickers Wellesley aircraft.
12 March 1938	Highest official speed by a motor-cycle at Brooklands; Eric Fernihough, on a 996cc Brough Superior covered one kilometre at 143.39 mph.
4 July 1939	Noel Pope made the fastest lap ever achieved by a motorcycle [124.51 mph].
22 June 1945	First flight of the Brooklands-built prototype Vickers Viking from Wisley airfield - the first postwar British airliner to enter service.
6 April 1948	First flight of the Nene Viking from Wisley - the World's first pure jet transport.
16 July 1948	First flight of the Vickers Viscount from Wisley - World's first turbo-prop airliner.
18 May 1951	First flight of the Vickers Valiant from Wisley - Britain's first four-jet 'V' bomber.
June 1962	First flight of a Vickers VC10 from Brooklands - largest jetliner built solely in the UK.
1978	British Aerospace Wind Tunnel tests for Richard Noble's Thrust II Land Speed Record attempt.

B

D

A   WORLDS FIRST FLIGHT
     TICKET OFFICE (RELOCATED)
B   BROOKLANDS AERO
     CLUBHOUSE
C   BROOKLANDS MEMORIAL
D   SITE OF VICKERS FACTORY

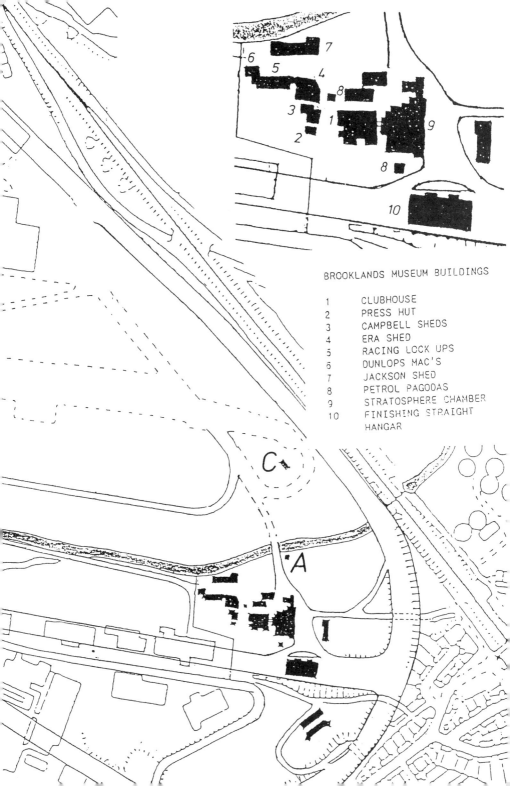

BROOKLANDS MUSEUM BUILDINGS

1	CLUBHOUSE
2	PRESS HUT
3	CAMPBELL SHEDS
4	ERA SHED
5	RACING LOCK UPS
6	DUNLOPS MAC'S
7	JACKSON SHED
8	PETROL PAGODAS
9	STRATOSPHERE CHAMBER
10	FINISHING STRAIGHT HANGAR

G.E. Buttriss:" Alexander Raby. A Surrey Ironmaster"
(WWLHS, Monograph No.34,1985)

G.B. Greenwood: "Walton and Weybridge. A Dictionary of
Local History" (Greenwood Publications, 3rd edn., 1978)

G.B. Greenwood: "Hersham in Surrey" (Greenwood
Publications, 1977)

G.B. Greenwood: "The Elmbridge Water Mills" (Privately
printed, 1980)

G.B. Greenwood: "An Account of the Royal Mills, Esher"
(EDLHS, Newsletter No. 21, July 1980)

J. Hillier: "Old Surrey Water Mills" (Skeffington, 1951)

Duncan James: "The Statue Foundry at Thames Ditton"
(Foundry Trades Journal, September 1972, pp.279-289)

Avril Lansdell: "If It Moves Film It. A History of Film
Making in Walton-on-Thames" (Weybridge Museums, 1973)

Avril Lansdell: "The Wey Navigation" (Elmbridge Borough
Council, 1975)

Michael Nash: "Early Seventeenth Century Schemes To Make
The Wey Navigable" (SAC,Vol.LXVI, 1969)

Metropolitan Water Board: "London's Water Supply 1903-1953.
A Review of the Metropolitan Water Board" (MWB, 1953)

E.S. Ormsby: "Engineering Works of Willans and Robinson"
(The Engineer, February 1965, pp.255-8)

Bernard Pardoe: "Ham Mills,Weybridge"
(WWLHS,Dialstone,No.64,February 1976)

Richard Sisley: "The London Water Supply. A Retrospect and
Summary".(Scientific Press,1899)

John A. Stonebanks:"The Thames Bridges at Walton"
(WWLHS,Paper No.4,1969)

John A. Stonebanks; "Enlightened Weybridge"
(WWLHS,Monograph No.19,1974)

John A. Stonebanks: "Electricity Undertakings in Walton and
Weybridge" (WWLHS,Monograph No.23,1975)

John A. Stonebanks:"The Thames at Walton and Weybridge"
(WWLHS,Paper No.18,1980)

John A. Stonebanks: "Cecil Milton Hepworth. Pioneer of Cinematography"(WWLHS,Monograph No.32,1984)

Paul W. Sowan: "Claygate's War Office Testing Ground" (SIHG, Newsletter No.24,December 1984)

David Taylor: "The Book of Cobham" (Barracuda Books, 1982)

Ann E. Tompson: "Milestones in the Esher District" (EDLHS, Newsletter No.21, July 1973)

Weybridge Museum: "Cinemas in Elmbridge" (Unpublished typescript file)

Geoffrey Wilson: "The Old Telegraphs" (Phillimore,1976)

Rowland G.M. Baker: "The Thames Bridges between Hampton Court and East Molesey" (SAC,VOL LVIII, 1961)

Rowland G.M. Baker: "East and West Molesey. A Dictionary of Local History" (Greenwood Publications, 1972)

Rowland G.M. Baker: "City Posts in the Elmbridge District" (EDLHS,Monograph No.7, 1980)

Abbreviations:-
    EDLHS - Esher District Local History Society
    MWB   - Metropolitan Water Board
    SAC   - Surrey Archaeological Collections
    SIHG   - Surrey Industrial History Group
    WWLHS - Walton and Weybridge Local History Society

ACKNOWLEDGEMENTS

The compiler acknowledges with thanks the invaluable and willing assistance of the following, all experts in their various fields: Mrs Mavis Collier and Miss Lesley Howes of the Painshill Park Trust; Mrs Avril Lansdell of Weybridge Museum; the late Cllr. George Greenwood of Hersham; Mr Paul Martin, Chairman of Walton and Weybridge Local History Society; and Mr David Taylor of Cobham.

R.G.M.B.

In addition, I would like to acknowledge with thanks the help given by the following:- Julian Temple of the Brooklands Museum, Dudley Geoghagan and A.J. Hutchings of the Brooklands Society, Professor Alan Crocker for proof reading, Rowena Oliver for producing nearly all of the line drawings from Rowland Baker's photographs, J.Kenneth Major and the Painshill Park trust for permission to use his drawing of the Painshill Park waterwheel and pumps, and finally Patrick and Pamela Haveron for their help in the final preparation of the artwork.

F.H.

The Surrey Industrial History Group are grateful to the Surrey Archaeological Society for their financial help in the publication of this book.

The Surrey Industrial History Group aims to study, record and, wherever appropriate, preserve the remains of the former industries of Surrey. The Group holds meetings, lectures, visits and social events, and publishes a regular Newsletter. Further information may be obtained from the Membership Secretary, SIHG, c/o The Surrey Archaeological Society, Castle Arch, Guildford, Surrey.